Goldilocks and the Three Bears

Phonics Consultant Susan Purcell

Illustrator Francesca Assirelli

Concept Fran Bromage

MILES KELLY

Once upon a time, there were three bears, who lived in a big house by a big wood.

Say the names as you spot each bear in the picture.

Daddy Bear

Mummy Bear

Baby Bear

There was Daddy Bear,
Mummy Bear and little
Baby Bear.

Sound out the things in the picture
beginning with **b** as you find them.

bear   ball   butterfly
    bush   basket

Every day, the bears liked to eat a lot of porridge for breakfast. One morning, it was too hot to eat.

Sound out these words with the o sound.

top   cot   fox   nod

job   dog   spot   clock

We will walk this way.

So the three bears left the house and went for a walk in the wood.

Spot the word that doesn't begin with the w sound.

web   won   wet   map   wig

Sound out the
initial blends
br, dr, gr
and tr

Among the trees, a girl called Goldilocks was growing worried.

She had drifted off a green, grassy trail and was trying to find her way home.

Say the names of the things in the picture, as you spot them.

branch   dress   grass   trunk

Goldilocks saw a **br**ick house with a **br**own door.

Inside, she could see the bears' **br**eakfast. As she was **gr**owing hungry and needed a **dr**ink, she went inside.

Spot the word that doesn't use the **br**, **dr**, **gr** or **tr** blend.

brush   drop   sheep   track

Highlight
the oa sound
(as in toast)

The table was loaded with food.
There were plates of toast and three
bowls of oat porridge too.

The porridge in the big red
bowl was much too hot.

The porridge in the medium
purple bowl was too lumpy.

Sound out these words, which all have the **oa** sound.

show   grow   hole   mole

coat   boat   toe

8

But the porridge in the small blue bowl was just right, so Goldilocks ate it all!

Say the words as you spot each bowl in the picture.

big red bowl

medium purple bowl

small blue bowl

As you read, focus on the ch sound (as in chair)

Next, Goldilocks went to explore. She saw three chairs – a big wooden chair, a medium purple chair and a small stripy chair.

Say the words as you spot each **chair** in the picture.

big **chair**

medium **chair**

small **chair**

When she tried the big chair it was much too hard.

The medium chair was much too soft, but the small chair was just right.

Sound out these words, which all have the **ch** sound.

chin   chop   chart   chick

rich   beach   church

Goldilocks sat on the little chair. In a flash, the chair broke, and Goldilocks fell on the floor with a crash.

Sound out these words, which all end with the **sh** sound.

cash   push   fish   dash

posh   rush   wish

Goldilocks didn't **stop**.
She **stood** up quickly, and
stamped up the **st**airs.

Emphasize the **st** blend, as you read

Spot the word that doesn't begin with **st**.

stick   sleep   stay   stuck

When Goldilocks got to the bedroom, she saw three beds. Feeling tired, she headed towards the big bed, but it was very hard.

The medium bed was very soft, but the small bed was just right.

Point to the red things in the picture.

Sound out these words with the **e** sound.

peg   shed   hen   egg

deaf   tread   bread   sweat

Say the words as you spot things with the **e** sound.

teddy

head

bed

Highlight the ng sound (as in walking)

Soon, the three bears arrived home. Walking had been hard work, so they were looking forward to eating a big breakfast.

Spot the word that doesn't use the **ng** ending.

feeling   reading

bedroom   talking

"Someone's been eating my porridge," said Daddy Bear, looking cross.

"Someone's been eating my porridge," said Mummy Bear, looking worried.

"Someone's been eating my porridge," said Baby Bear, looking sad. "And they've eaten it all up!"

Emphasize the **ng** sound as you say this sentence together.

"Someone's been eating my porridge," said Baby Bear.

Next, the three bears saw their three chairs.

"Someone's been sitting in my chair," said Daddy Bear.

"Someone's been sitting in my chair," said Mummy Bear.

"Someone's been sitting in my chair," said Baby Bear. "And they've broken it into bits!"

Spot the word that doesn't end in the **air** sound.

hair   stair   pair   door   fair

18

Then the three bears went upstairs.

"Someone's been sleeping in my bed," said Daddy Bear.

"Someone's been sleeping in my bed," said Mummy Bear.

Sound out these words with the **air** sound.

bear   spare   dare   care

square   where   there

"Someone's been sleeping in my bed," said Baby Bear. "And they're still lying there!"

When Goldilocks saw the bears, she got quite a fright, and gave a cry!

Sound out these words with the **ie** sound.

pie   tie   sigh   high
try   fry   like   bike   eye

20

Spot the word that doesn't use the **ie** sound.

sky   spy   dry
big   night   right

Emphasize the r sound (as in ran)

Goldilocks raced right out of the house. She ran away really fast and the three bears never saw her again.

Spot the word that doesn't begin with the r sound.

rat   rain   rug   nod   red

Ask your child to **retell** the story using
these key sounds and story images.

hot

walk

breakfast

bowl

chair

bed

looking

cry

ran

Say the words in each line out loud together.
Can you **think** of another word that uses the highlighted **sound**?

basket   bush   ball   bear

drink   drifted   dress   drop

grip   growing   green   grass

trunk   trees   track   trail

fish   rush   smash   dash

stick   stood   stop   stay

feeling   looking   eating   sleeping

bear   hair   care   their

high   bike   cry   tie

You've had fun with phonics! Well done.